Red Kites

naturally scottish

SCOTTISH NATURAL HERITAGE

© Scottish Natural Heritage 2001

ISBN 1 85397 061 1 paperback

A CIPO record is held at the British Library

L4K0601

Acknowledgements:

Authors: David Minns (RSPB) and Doug Gilbert (SNH)

Series Editor: Andy Douse (SNH)

Design and production: SNH Design and Publications

Text © Scottish Natural Heritage & Royal Society for the Protection of Birds

Photographs:

C. Gomersall/RSPB front cover, back cover, frontispiece, 2, 7, 8, 14, 18, 19, 20 bottom, **M. Hamblin** vii, 10, **L. Campbell/SNH** contents, 5, 13, **L. Gill/SNH** 3, 9 bottom, **M. Lane/Woodfall Wild Images** 15, 16, 20 top, 21

Illustrations:

J. Ritchie/Cambridge University Press *The Influence of Man on Animal Life in Scotland (Fig 3.3)*, 9 top, **J. Tasker** 4, 6, 11

Scottish Natural Heritage

Design and Publications

Battleby

Redgorton

Perth PH1 3EW

Tel: 01738 444177

Fax: 01738 827411

E-mail: pubs@snh.gov.uk

Web site: http://www.snh.org.uk

Cover photograph:
Red Kite in flight

Red Kites

naturally scottish

by

David Minns & Doug Gilbert

Foreword

For most of my bird-watching life, I had to travel to deepest Wales to see the few surviving red kites or just be content to read the likes of the Reverend Forsythe extolling the beauty of the salmon-tailed gleds of Victorian times. In his day, he enjoyed watching them gliding over the golden fields of corn stooks in Strathspey searching for mice.

I saw my first red kite in Scotland in 1972, quartering the grey winter fields of the upper Spey. It was just a wandering vagrant but it did kindle my hopes that one day they would be back. That year there were only 12 pairs of ospreys in the growing Scottish population and the re-introduction of the white-tailed sea eagle was still a dream.

By the late 1980s, ospreys had climbed to sixty pairs and the first few pairs of sea eagles were breeding in western Scotland. It was time to bring back the gled and this book tells that story. I can recall the thrills and difficulties of that exciting project.

Unforgettable was the enthusiasm of the Swedish ornithologists as they took me to kite nests in the woods of Skanor in 1989. I remember five summer visits with long days of tree climbing, the rufous beauty of the kites soaring over green beech trees and the beautiful singing of thrush nightingales as we collected young kites destined for Scotland.

At home, it was so rewarding to see the interest in the kites from local people living on the Black Isle. Farmers and crofters putting out dead rabbits to feed the new arrivals, and woodland owners so obviously thrilled and protective of the first nests. Along with that, the kites seemed so at home.

I particularly remember standing with former RSPB staff member Colin Crooke near Neil Gunn's monument above Dingwall checking an early winter roost. Below us forty kites wheeled in the grey November dusk against a hazy backdrop of church spires and smoking chimneys. We marvelled that only eight years earlier there had been no kites in Scotland.

Roy Dennis
Former RSPB Regional Officer - Highlands

Contents

Introduction

Absent from Scotland's skies for over a century following human persecution, red kites are slowly making a comeback thanks to an exciting project to re-introduce them from mainland Europe. These elegant birds of prey, with a wingspan of almost two metres, pose no threat to game-rearing or farming interests, being mostly carrion eaters. Following the release of young kites brought in from Sweden and, more recently, eastern Germany, they have successfully begun to re-colonise northern and central Scotland. Hopefully, it will not be long before the sight of the red kite can be enjoyed by many people throughout the country.

Appearance

Red kites are long-winged, long-tailed birds of prey, about
the size of large gulls. They have narrower wings than
buzzards, and distinctive forked tails, features which mean
their flight is buoyant and graceful, even acrobatic at
times. In good light, the chestnut colouring of the body
and upper tail feathers contrast with the pale grey head,
black wing tips and white underwing patches. Together
these characters combine to make red kites distinctive,
even at long distances.

In common with many birds of prey,
female kites are slightly larger than
males. This is thought to be an
adaptation to reduce competition
between the sexes for food, although
it may also be connected with
the female's greater commitment to
defend the nest.

Habitat

In Britain we tend to think of red kites as birds of remote hilly areas because of their confinement for the last hundred years to the hills of rural Wales. However, in other countries they are much more widespread than this, living mainly in well-wooded farmland below 600 metres (2000 feet) altitude. This seems to be the case in Scotland as well, with nests often found near the edges of woods or copses so that feeding habitat is easily available on surrounding farmland and pastures. In England, red kites are characteristically birds of lowland mixed farmland where there are plenty of trees for nesting and roosting.

Feeding

Red kites are mainly scavengers, eating a wide range of carrion. The feeding habits of the new Scottish population are being studied in detail as part of the re-introduction project. Researchers record the type of food remains at nests, as well as pellets of indigestible prey remains found below perches and at roosts. These studies show that their most common food by far is dead rabbits, with other carrion, such as dead sheep and shot pheasants, also eaten regularly. Kites will hunt live prey such as voles and mice, and sometimes young crows and pigeons are taken from their nests. However, red kites have never been known to kill lambs either here in Britain or on the continent, they are in fact incapable of doing so. Like buzzards, a substantial part of their diet consists of invertebrates, such as earthworms, beetles, moth larvae and crane flies.

Kites forage for carrion by soaring and circling to locate food and then diving steeply towards it, but much of their food is taken on the ground. They also 'pirate' food from other birds such as crows, kestrels and buzzards. On the continent, and increasingly in Britain, they are commonly seen along roads looking for animals killed by passing traffic.

Kites occasionally eat dead rats found around farms, and so are vulnerable to a build up of poisons (rodenticides) used by farmers for legal pest-control.

Percentage Occurence of Prey Items in 40 Red Kite Pellets from Northern Scotland (from data in Wildman, O'Toole and Summers [1998])

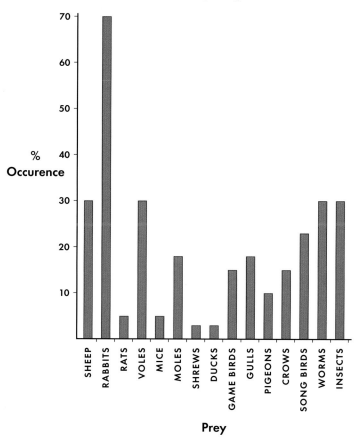

Prey

Breeding

Red kites usually nest in mature coniferous or broadleaved trees where they build loose, untidy nests about 30 to 40 feet off the ground. Nests are generally re-used from year to year and they can reach a metre in diameter when used for several years in succession. Old crow and buzzard nests are also adopted. Nests where kites have been successful in raising young are much more likely to be re-used than unsuccessful ones. Nests are constructed of dead twigs, mostly brought in by the male, and lined with grass, other vegetation and tufts of sheep's wool. Kites have long been known to d their nests with odd materials.

Shakespeare warned in *A Winter's Tale* "When a kite builds, look to lesser linen" in recognition of their tendency to take underwear from washing lines! Present-day nests in Scotland have been found to contain black silage bags, plastic shopping bags, old newspapers, disposable nappies, burst balloons, tinfoil and other shiny materials.

The birds generally breed for the first time when they are two or three years old with the same pair bond being renewed each spring. In England and Scotland, a small number of re-introduced birds have bred after only one year. Nesting generally starts in late March or early April, with usually 1-3 eggs being laid. There have however been several broods of four young in both English and Scottish red kite nests - an indication that habitat conditions are good for them. The female does most of the incubating, which lasts around 31 days, while the male provides the female and young with food at the nest.

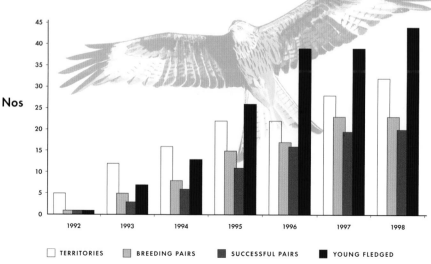

The Number of Red Kites Breeding in Northern Scotland from 1992-98

Nos

□ TERRITORIES ▨ BREEDING PAIRS ▨ SUCCESSFUL PAIRS ■ YOUNG FLEDGED

The young leave the nest after about 50 days, and then spend a further 15–20 days being fed by their parents nearby before becoming self-sufficient. The last young leave the nest in mid or late July. In their first two years young kites disperse quite widely, but to breed they usually return to areas where they were born.

During the breeding season territories often overlap and only the immediate vicinity of the nest is defended. This tendency to be semi-colonial has meant that the rate at which nesting kites have spread out from the original re-introduction sites in Scotland and England has been slow. Outwith the breeding season, kites often roost communally. In parts of Europe up to 500 birds have been recorded at a single roost while in Scotland, roosts have contained as many as 50 birds.

History of the red kite in Britain

When woodland covered Britain after the last Ice Age, the red kite was probably limited to areas with naturally occurring open land. As agriculture developed and expanded, increasing areas of open habitat were created over which the birds could forage. This association between people, farming and red kites remains central to the success of red kites in Britain.

By the beginning of the 19th century the red kite bred throughout Britain, apart from some areas in south-east England. It was relatively common in much of lowland Scotland, scavenging on rubbish and carrion around farmsteads and towns, and nesting in nearby woods. The old Scots name for the kite is gled (also known as the gledd, glead, glade or swallow-tailed or salmon-tailed gled) derived from the same Saxon verb as the modern word 'glide'. The name survives in place names such as Gladsmuir in East Lothian, Glede Knowe near Innerleithen and Gladsfield north of Perth. Burns, in his celebrated song *Killiecrankie*, says:

> *"Or I had fed an Athole gled*
> *On the braes o' Killiecrankie, O!"*

The gaelic names of the kite include clamhan gobhlach and croman lochaidh meaning fork-tailed hawk or hawk of the sheeps fleece. James Ritchie writing in 1920, in *The Influence of Man on Animal Life in Scotland*, mentions the "Clach-a-chambain or 'Gled Stone', such as that at the head of Glen Brierachan near Pitlochry, mark[ing] a well remembered perching place of the Gled."

Harvie-Brown, the great Victorian ornithologist of Scotland, lamented in his book *A Fauna of the Tay Basin and Strathmore* that there was a "frequent confusion in the application of the names 'Gled' or 'Glede'. ...I have come across many instances of this confusion between Kites and Buzzards by these names, and some huge blunders in consequence thereof."

Distribution

The red kite has a relatively restricted world distribution. They are almost entirely confined to Europe apart from small, isolated populations in north-west Africa and the Caucasus. Parts of France, eastern Germany and Spain support healthy populations, with sparser numbers occurring from southern Sweden to Sicily and from the Canary Islands to the shores of the Black Sea. In Europe, red kites share their range with migratory black kites - a species with a much wider distribution that also includes Asia, Africa and Australia. In mainland Europe, with its more severe winter weather, first year red kites often migrate southwards, but in Britain our milder climate makes this unnecessary.

Over the last 100 – 150 years there has been a marked decline in both the range and numbers of red kites in many areas, partly because of human persecution but also because of adverse habitat changes in some areas of Europe. In eastern Germany, recent political changes have brought about an intensification of agriculture which has led to a decline in the availability of their main natural food with consequent declines in red kite populations.

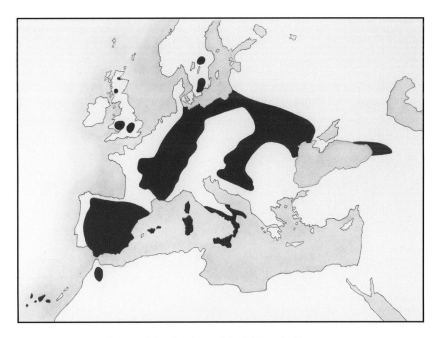

Recent Distribution of Red Kites in Europe

The re-introduction project

Having been accepted and even welcomed as scavengers which helped keep streets clean in mediaeval times, an Act of James II in 1457 listed kites as vermin which should be destroyed. Quoted in James Ritchie's book, the Act provides for the destruction of "foulys of rief," being "ruikes, crawes, eirnes, bissettes, gleddes, mittalles, the whilk destroyes beast, corn and wilde foulys". They "sall utterly be destroyed by all manner of men, be all engine of all manner of crafts that may be founden" since "the slauchter of them sall cause great multitude of divers kind of wilde foulys for man's sustentacion."

By the 1860s the increase in Victorian gamekeeping, which did not tolerate birds of prey, meant that red kites were only found regularly in Inverness-shire, Perthshire and Aberdeenshire. Gamekeepers' 'vermin' records show, for example, that 105 red kites were killed in the Callander Hills between December 1824 and December 1825. The red kite is believed to have become extinct as a breeding species in Scotland around 1880. In England, much the same pattern was followed with the last kites thought to have nested in Shropshire in the 1870s. Meanwhile, a small population clung on in the valleys of mid-Wales, reaching an all-time low of under twenty birds

in the 1930s. Red kites managed to persist in Wales largely because there was far less game shooting. During the second half of the 20th century the Welsh kite population slowly expanded, thanks to dedicated protection by red kite enthusiasts, but it became increasingly clear that re-colonisation of the rest of Britain was going to take a very long time. Plans were therefore drawn up to re-introduce kites to Scotland and England from healthy populations in mainland Europe.

Moving animals around the world can have disastrous effects - as shown by the introduction of rabbits to Australia - so there are stringent criteria that need to be satisfied before carrying out a re-introduction project. Amongst these, the species must have occurred in the area naturally in the past; the habitat must be suitable for it once again to live there; it must have become extinct because of man's actions; and the conditions which led to its extinction must no longer prevail. This last criterion posed some problems because, whilst attitudes towards kites are now very much more enlightened than during the 19th century, other birds of prey are still regarded by some as a threat to sporting and farming interests. Poisoned baits are still being placed illegally to kill birds of prey. Being a scavenger, the red kite is extremely

vulnerable to this practice and 22 Scottish kites have been confirmed poisoned since the first re-introduction in 1989. Unlike almost any other country in the world, the damaging pastime of egg collecting also still persists in Britain. Red kites eggs, because of their rarity, are sought after as trophies by collectors who, pose a serious threat to the breeding effort of these birds. Despite these reservations, it was thought likely that red kites could re-establish themselves in suitable areas of Britain, if given a helping hand.

In 1989, the then Nature Conservancy Council (now Scottish Natural Heritage in Scotland and English Nature in England), and the Royal Society for the Protection of Birds (RSPB) began a programme to re-introduce red kites to Scotland and England. Young kites from Sweden (93 in number), eastern Germany (97) and Spain (93) were brought across to supply the re-introduction programmes for northern and central Scotland,

the Midlands and southern England. Kept in large release cages in remote woodland for about a month until fully fledged, they were then released into the wild after veterinary checks. In northern Scotland breeding first occurred in 1992, with the rearing of a single chick - the first in Scotland for over 100 years.

Although nesting numbers in southern England and northern Scotland began to build up steadily, the semi-colonial nature of kites once again asserted itself, and it became clear that re-colonisation of the whole of their former range would take a very long time. Accordingly, a second release site in the English Midlands was set up in 1995, followed by one in central Scotland in 1996. These have also been successful, with kites starting to nest in these areas in 1997 and 1998 respectively.

Red kites and the law

Like all birds of prey, red kites in Scotland are protected by the Wildlife & Countryside Act 1981 at all times of year. Indeed, such is their rarity that offences against them, their eggs or young are subject to higher penalties than is the case with more common species. Not only is it illegal to kill kites or take their eggs, an offence is also committed if someone wilfully disturbs them at the nest or with unflown young. It is, of course, also illegal to place poisoned baits in open countryside, whether or not the intended victim is a protected species. It can also be an offence to be in possession of a dead kite (including stuffed birds) without appropriate authority.

The future

At last, the fortunes of red kites throughout Britain are on the up. The re-introduced populations in Scotland and England, and the remnant Welsh population of native British kites are all showing strong signs of success. A survey in the year 2000 estimated that the total number of breeding pairs of kites in the UK was 429. For the first time in perhaps 300 years, the number of red kites in Britain is increasing significantly. Their breeding success is good and they are slowly and steadily expanding. The decision to release kites in ecologically rich areas of mixed farmland on the Black Isle and central Scotland has been vindicated. Further re-introduction points are being considered to aid the restoration of the birds to their former widespread range. It is unlikely that they will ever return to their role as city street scavengers, but with so much habitat apparently suitable for them in Scotland they will surely become a common enough sight in time in many lowland and upland areas.

Despite the continued risk of accidental and regretably, deliberate poisoning, attitudes towards the destruction of birds of prey have changed considerably. Those who live with red kites know they pose no threat to game or livestock interests. They are welcomed by the vast majority of farmers, landowners and tourist-based businesses. Continuing changes in the farming landscape, helped by Government funded incentive schemes such as the Rural Stewardship Scheme and Farm Woodland Premium Scheme, are creating better conditions for red kites. As they become more common, we can look forward to their acrobatic, gliding flight becoming an increasingly familiar sight, and the "swallow-tailed gled" will once more be a frequent and inspiring addition to Scotland's countryside. The future looks bright for the red kite in Scotland!

How can I help?

If you live in an area with kites, and regularly use poison to control rodent problems on a farm or other business, please pay special regard to good practice in using rodenticides and disposing of the rodent remains. Ask for a copy of the RSPB leaflet on this subject available from your local RSPB office (see contact details below).

Nearly all the young kites fledged in Scotland are presently marked with coloured wing-tags, to aid individual identification and allow detailed research into bird movements and behaviour. If you see a kite, you can help. First see what colour the tags are (colours may differ on each wing), and if possible read the symbols on them. Write down the date and place you saw the kite along with any tag details. Then please pass this information, as soon as possible, to any of the following RSPB offices:

North Scotland,
Etive House,
Beechwood Park,
Inverness
IV2 3BW
Tel 01463 715000
nsro@rspb.org.uk

East Scotland,
10 Albyn Terrace,
Aberdeen
AB10 1YP
Tel 01224 624824
esro@rspb.org.uk

South & West Scotland,
Unit 3.1,
West of Scotland Science Park,
Kelvin Campus,
Glasgow G20 0SP
Tel 0141 576 4100
swsro@rspb.org.uk

All sightings will be useful in helping to track the birds' movements and monitor their survival.

RSPB Scotland Headquarters, Dunedin House, 25 Ravelstone Terrace, Edinburgh EH4 3TP
Tel 0131 311 6500 Fax 0131 311 6569 E-mail: rspb.scotland@rspb.org.uk Web: www.rspb.org.uk

Where can I see red kites in Scotland?

With an increase in the number of birds in central Scotland it will not be too long before they are a regular sight there but at present, numbers are relatively low and they are not as easy to see as birds north of Inverness. A public viewing site has been set up in the Tourist Information Centre at North Kessock, just north of Inverness. Here visitors can watch close-up TV pictures from a nearby nest during the breeding season (April to June), as well as recordings of previous year's pairs. There is also information on where the birds can be seen flying locally.

Further reading

The Red Kite by Roger Lovegrove, RSPB 1995

Population Ecology of Raptors by Ian Newton, Poyser 1979

The diet and foraging behaviour of the Red Kite in northern Scotland
by L Wildman, L O'Toole & R W Summers: Scottish Birds 19; 134-140. 1998

Support for the re-introduction programme in Scotland

SNH and RSPB wish to thank those landowners who have welcomed the kite release cages onto their land, and the neighbouring landowners, gamekeepers, farmers and foresters who have contributed to the success of the red kite re-introduction project. Our gratitude is also due to the donor countries: the Environmental Protection Board in Sweden and the Ministry of the Environment in Sachsen-Anhalt in Germany. British Airways Assisting Conservation Programme provided free air transport from Germany. RAF Kinloss provided invaluable assistance with the transport of the first birds from Sweden. Others who assisted the re-introduction projects include HM Customs & Excise at Glasgow; Universities of Aberdeen and Nottingham, Professor Doctor M. Stubbe of the University of Halle-Wittenberg, Germany; WWF-Sweden; Vogelschutzwarte Steckby; Skanes Ornithologiska Forening; Parks Car and Van Hire; Scottish Raptor Study Groups; Forest Enterprise and the British Airports Authority in Glasgow.

Also in the Naturally Scottish series...

If you have enjoyed Red Kites why not find out more about Scotland's wildlife in our Naturally Scottish series. Each booklet looks at one or more of Scotland's native species. The clear and informative text is illustrated with exceptional photographs by top wildlife photographers, showing the species in their native habitats and illustrating their relationships with man. They also provide information on conservation and the law.

Corncrakes

Secretive, skulking, rasping, loud, tuneless, scarce. . . all these words have been used to describe the corncrake. But once you could have added plentiful and widespread to the list. Now only a few birds visit Scotland each year. This booklet brings you the latest information on the corncrake and reveals this elusive and noisy bird in its grassy home.
ISBN 1 85397 049 2 pbk 40pp £3.95

Red Squirrels

The red squirrel is one Scotland's most endearing mammals. This booklet provides an insight into their ecology and some of the problems facing red squirrels in Scotland today.
Peter Lurz & Mairi Cooper
ISBN 1 85397 298 4 pbk 20pp £3.00

Badgers

With its distinctive black and white striped face and short, squat body, the badger is probably one of the most popular mammals in Britain. Packed with stunning photographs, this publication reveals some amazing facts about the shy, secretive badger.
Mairi Cooper & John Ralston
ISBN 1 85397 254 1 pbk 16pp £3.00

Burnet Moths

Unlike many other species of moth, burnet moths fly by day. They can be easily recognised by their beautiful, glossy black wings with crimson spots. Their striking colouring is a very real warning to predators.
Mark Young
ISBN 1 85397 209 6 pbk 24pp £3.00

Sea Eagles

This magnificent bird, with its wing span of over 2m is the largest bird of prey in Britain. In 1916 they became extinct, but a reintroduction programme began in 1975. This booklet documents the return of this truly majestic eagle. Production subsidised by Anheuser-Busch.
Greg Mudge, Kevin Duffy, Kate Thompson & John Love
ISBN 1 85397 208 8 pbk 16pp £1.50

Seals

All around the coasts of Scotland grey and common seals can be found basking on the rocks, resting between fishing expeditions. Gain an insight into how seals live, their amazing grace and elegance in water contrasted to their clumsiness on land, and where and when you can watch seals in Scotland.
Elizabeth Cruwys and John Baxter
ISBN 1 85397 233 9 pbk 24pp £3.00

Whales, Dolphins & Porpoises

About one-third of the species of whales, dolphins and porpoises known world-wide have been recorded in British waters and 15 species have been found there regularly. Find out how they live, where they can be seen and how they are affected by pollution.
Sandy Kerr (ed.)
ISBN 1 85397 210 X pbk 24pp £3.00

SNH Publications Order Form:
Naturally Scottish Series

Title	Price	Quantity
Corncrakes	£3.95	
Red Squirrels	£3.00	
Badgers	£3.00	
Burnet Moths	£3.00	
Sea Eagles	£1.50	
Seals	£3.00	
Whales, Dolphins & Porpoises	£3.00	

Postage and packing: free of charge in the UK, a standard charge of £2.95 will be applied to all orders from the European Union. Elsewhere a standard charge of £5.50 will be applied for postage.

Please complete in BLOCK CAPITALS

Name _____

Address _____

_____

_____

_____ Post Code _____

Type of Credit Card   EUROCARD MasterCard ☐   VISA ☐

Name of card holder _____

Card Number ☐☐☐☐ ☐☐☐☐ ☐☐☐☐ ☐☐☐☐

Expiry Date ☐☐ ☐☐

Send order and cheque made payable to Scottish Natural Heritage to:

Scottish Natural Heritage. Design and Publications, Battleby, Redgorton, Perth PH1 3EW

pubs@snh.gov.uk
www.snh.org.uk

Please add my name to the mailing list for the: SNH Magazine ☐

Publications Catalogue ☐